HEY, PEANUTS!

Selected Cartoons From
MORE PEANUTS
Vol. 2

by Charles M. Schulz

A Crest Reprint

CREST
BOOK

Fawcett Publications, Inc., Greenwich, Conn.
Member of American Book Publishers Council, Inc.

HEY, PEANUTS!

This book, prepared especially for Fawcett Publications, Inc.,
comprises the second half of MORE PEANUTS, and is published
by arrangement with Holt, Rinehart and Winston, Inc.

First Crest printing, November 1962

Crest Books are published by Fawcett World Library,
67 West 44th Street, New York 36, New York.
Printed in the United States of America.

SCHULZ

AND THERE GOES CHARLIE BROWN THRU RIGHT GUARD!

HE SHAKES OFF ONE TACKLER.. AND ANOTHER.. TEARING.. TWISTING.. TURNING..

AND NOW HE'S IN THE CLEAR! HE'S..HE'S... HE'S....

SCHULZ.